CONTENTS

ITALO
CALVINO

TEN ITALIAN FOLKTALES

TRANSLATED BY GEORGE MARTIN

PENGUIN BOOKS

PENGUIN BOOKS

Published by the Penguin Group. Penguin Books Ltd, 27 Wrights Lane, London
w8 5tz, England. Penguin Books USA Inc., 375 Hudson Street, New York, New
York 10014, USA. Penguin Books Australia Ltd, Ringwood, Victoria, Australia.
Penguin Books Canada Ltd, 10 Alcorn Avenue, Toronto, Ontario, Canada m4v 3b2.
Penguin Books (NZ) Ltd, 182–190 Wairau Road, Auckland 10, New Zealand ·
Penguin Books Ltd, Registered Offices: Harmondsworth, Middlesex, England ·
These stories are taken from *Italian Folktales: Selected and Retold by Italo
Calvino*, published by Penguin Books in 1982. This edition published 1995 ·
Copyright 1956 by Giulio Einaudi Editore S.p.A. This translation copyright ©
Harcourt Brace Jovanovich, Inc., 1980. All rights reserved · Typeset by Datix
International Limited, Bungay, Suffolk · Printed in England by Clays Ltd, St Ives
plc · Except in the United States of America, this book is sold subject to the
condition that it shall not, by way of trade or otherwise, be lent, re-sold, hired out,
or otherwise circulated without the publisher's prior consent in any form of
binding or cover other than that in which it is published and without a similar
condition including this condition being imposed on the subsequent purchaser ·
10 9 8 7 6 5 4 3 2 1

Crack and Crook

In a distant town there was a famous thief known as Crack, whom nobody had ever been able to catch. The main ambition of this Crack was to meet Crook, another notorious thief, and form a partnership with him. One day as Crack was eating lunch at the tavern across the table from a stranger, he went to look at his watch and found it missing. The only person in the world who could have taken it without my knowing, he thought, is Crook. So what did Crack do but turn right around and steal Crook's purse. When the stranger got ready to pay for his lunch, he found his purse gone and said to his table companion, 'Well, well, you must be Crack.'

'And you must be Crook.'

'Right.'

'Fine, we'll work together.'

They went to the city and made for the king's treasury, which was completely surrounded by guards. The thieves therefore dug an underground tunnel into the treasury and stole everything. Surveying his loss, the king had no idea how he might catch the robbers. He went to a man named Snare, who had been put in prison for stealing, and said, 'If you can tell me who committed this robbery, I'll set you free and make you a marquis.'

Snare replied, 'It can be none other than Crack or Crook, or both of them together, since they are the most notorious thieves alive. But I'll tell you how you can catch them. Have the price of meat raised to one hundred dollars a pound. The person who pays that much for it will be your thief.'

The king had the price of meat raised to one hundred dollars a pound, and everybody stopped buying meat. Finally it was reported that a friar had gone to a certain butcher and bought meat. Snare said, 'That had to be Crack or Crook in disguise. I'll now disguise myself and go around to the houses begging. If anybody gives me meat, I'll make a red mark on the front door, and your guards can go and arrest the thieves.'

But when he made a red mark on Crack's house, the thief saw it and went and marked all the other doors in the city with red, so there was no telling in the end where Crack and Crook lived.

Snare said to the king, 'Didn't I tell you they were foxy? But there's someone else foxier than they are. Here's the next thing to do: put a tub of boiling pitch at the bottom of the treasury steps. Whoever goes down to steal will fall right into it, and his dead body will give him away.'

Crack and Crook had run out of money in the meantime and decided to go back to the treasury for more. Crook went in first, but it was dark, and he fell into the tub. Crack came along and tried to pull his friend's body out of the pitch, but it stuck fast in the tub. He then cut off the head and carried it away.

The next day the king went to see if he had caught the thief. 'This time we got him! We got him!' But the corpse had no head, so they were none the wiser about the thief or any accomplices he might have had.

Snare said, 'There's one more thing we can do: have the dead man dragged through the city by two horses. The house where you hear somebody weeping has to be the thief's house.'

In effect, when Crook's wife looked out the window and saw her husband's body being dragged through the street, she began screaming and crying. But Crack was there and knew right away that would be their undoing. He therefore started smashing dishes right and left and thrashing the poor woman at the same time. Attracted by all that screaming, the guards came in and found a man beating his wife for breaking up all the dishes in the house.

The king then had a decree posted on every street corner that he would pardon the thief who had robbed him, if the thief now managed to steal the sheets out from under him at night. Crack came forward and said he could do it.

That night the king undressed and went to bed with his gun to wait for the thief. Crack got a dead body from a gravedigger, dressed it in his own clothes, and carried it to the roof of the royal palace. At midnight the cadaver, held by a rope, was dangling before the king's windows. Thinking it was Crack, the king fired one shot and watched him fall, cord and all. He ran downstairs to see if he was dead. While the king was gone, Crack slipped into his room and stole the sheets. He was therefore pardoned, and so that he wouldn't have to steal any longer, the king married his daughter to him.

The Land Where One Never Dies

One day a young man said, 'This tale about everybody having to die doesn't set too well with me. I will go in search of the land where one never dies.'

He bid father, mother, uncles, and cousins goodbye and departed. For days and months he walked, asking everybody he met if they could direct him to the place where one never dies. But no one knew of any such place. One day he met an old man with a white beard down to his chest, pushing a wheelbarrow full of rocks. The boy asked him, 'Could you direct me to that place where one never dies?'

'You don't want to die? Stick with me. Until I've finished carting away that entire mountain rock by rock, you shall not die.'

'How long will it take you to level it?'

'One hundred years at least.'

'And I'll have to die afterward?'

'I'm afraid so.'

'No, this is no place for me. I will go to the place where one *never* dies.'

He said goodbye to the old man and pushed onward. 5

He walked for miles and came to a forest so vast that it seemed endless. There he saw an old man with a beard down to his navel pruning branches with a pruning hook. The young man asked, 'Could you kindly tell me of a place where one never dies?'

'Stick with me,' replied the old man. 'Until I've trimmed all the trees in this forest with my pruning hook, you shall not die.'

'How long will that take?'

'Who knows? At least two hundred years.'

'And afterward I'll still have to die?'

'Indeed you will. Isn't two hundred years enough for you?'

'No, this is no place for me. I'm seeking a place where one *never* dies.'

They said goodbye, and the youth continued onward. A few months later he reached the seashore. There he saw an old man with a beard down to his knees watching a duck drink seawater.

'Could you kindly tell me of a place where one never dies?'

'If you're afraid to die, stick with me. See that duck? Until it has drunk the sea dry, there's no danger at all of your dying.'

'How long will it take?'

'Roughly three hundred years.'

'And afterward I'll have to die?'

'What else do you expect? How much longer would you even want to live?'

'No, no, no. Not even this place is for me. I must go where one *never* dies.'

He resumed his journey. One evening he came to a magnificent palace. He knocked, and the door was opened by an old man with a beard all the way down to his feet. 'What is it you look for, young man?'

'I'm looking for the place where one never dies.'

'Good for you, you've found it! This is the place where one never dies. As long as you stay with me, you can bet your boots you won't die.'

'At last, after all the miles I've trudged! This is just the place I was seeking! But are you sure I'm not imposing on you?'

'Absolutely. I'm delighted to have company.'

So the youth moved into the palace with the old man and lived like a lord. The years went by so fast and so pleasantly that he lost all track of time. Then one day he said to the old man, 'There's no place on earth like here, but I really would like to pay my family a little visit and see how they're getting along.'

'What family are you talking about? The last of your relatives died quite some time ago.'

'I'd still like to go on a little journey, if only to revisit 7 my birthplace and possibly run into the sons of my relatives' sons.'

'If you're bent on going, follow my instructions. Go to the stable and get my white horse, which gallops like the wind. But once you're on him, never, never dismount for any reason whatever, or you will die on the spot.'

'Don't worry, I'll stay in the saddle. You know how I hate the very idea of dying!'

He went to the stable, led out the white horse, got into the saddle, and was off like the wind. He passed the place where he had met the old man with the duck. There where the sea used to be was now a vast prairie. On the edge of it was a little pile of bones, the bones of the old man. 'Just look at that,' said the youth. 'I was wise not to tarry here, or I too would now be dead.'

He moved on and came to what was once the vast forest where the old man had to prune every single tree with his pruning hook. Not one tree was left, and the ground was as bare as a desert. 'How right I was not to stop here, or I too would now be long gone, like the old soul in the forest.'

He passed the place where the huge mountain had stood, which an old man was to cart away rock by rock. Now the ground was as level as a billiard table.

'Nor would I have fared any better here!'

8   On and on he went, finally reaching his town, but it

had changed so much he no longer recognized it. Not only was his house gone, but even the street it had stood on. He inquired about his relatives, but no one had ever heard his family name. That was the end of it. 'I might as well go back at once,' he decided.

He turned his horse around and started back, but was not halfway home before he met a carter with a cart full of old shoes and drawn by an ox. 'Sir,' said the carter, 'please be so kind as to dismount for a moment and help me dislodge this wheel sticking in the mud.'

'I'm in a hurry and can't get out of the saddle,' replied the youth.

'Please help me. I'm all by myself, as you can see, and night is coming on.'

Moved to pity, the youth dismounted. He had only one foot on the ground and the other still in the stirrup, when the carter grabbed him by the arm and said: 'I have you at last! Know who I am? Yes, I am Death! See all those old shoes in the cart? They're all the pairs you caused me to wear out running after you. Now you've fallen into my hands, from which no one ever escapes!'

So the poor young man had to die the same as everybody else.

Pome and Peel

There was once a noble couple that longed to have a son, but alas, they had none. One day the lord was abroad and encountered a wizard. 'Sir Wizard,' he said, 'please tell me what I can do to have a son.'

The wizard gave him an apple and said, 'Have your wife eat it, and at the end of nine months she will give birth to a fine baby boy.'

The husband took the apple home to his wife. 'Eat this apple, and we will have a fine baby boy. A wizard told me so.'

Overjoyed, the wife called her maidservant and told her to peel the apple. The maidservant did so, but kept the peeling and ate it herself.

A son was born to the lady, and on the same day a son was born to her maidservant. The maidservant's son was as ruddy as an apple skin; the lady's son was as white as apple pulp. The lord looked on them both as his sons and reared and schooled them together.

Growing up, Pome and Peel loved each other like brothers. Out walking one day, they heard about a wizard's daughter as dazzling as the sun; but no one had ever seen her, as she never went abroad or even looked out her window. Pome and Peel had a large bronze horse built with a hollow belly, and they hid in it with a trumpet and a violin. The horse moved on wheels the boys turned from inside, and in that manner they rolled up to the wizard's palace and began to play. The wizard looked out and, seeing that wonderful bronze horse making music all by itself, invited it inside to entertain his daughter.

The maiden was delighted. But the minute she was left alone with the horse, out stepped Pome and Peel, and she was quite frightened. 'Don't be afraid,' they said to her. 'We heard how beautiful you are, and we just had to see you. If you want us to leave, we will. But if you like our music and want us to keep playing, we'll do so, then depart without letting anyone know we were ever here.'

So they stayed on, playing and having a good time, and after a while the wizard's daughter didn't want them to leave. 'Come with us,' Pome told her, 'and I'll marry you.'

She accepted. They all hid in the horse's belly and off they rolled. No sooner had they gone than the wizard returned home, called his daughter, looked for her, questioned the guard at the gate: there was no sign of her anywhere. Then he realized he had been tricked, and he was furious. He went to the balcony and screamed three curses on the girl: 'Let her come upon three horses – one white, one red, one black – and loving horses the way she does, let her leap on the white one, and let this horse be her undoing.

'Or else: Let her come upon three pretty little dogs – one white, one red, one black – and loving little black dogs the way she does, let her pick up the black one, and let this dog be her undoing.

'Or else: On the night she goes to bed with her spouse, let a giant snake come through the window, and let this snake be her undoing.'

While the wizard was screaming those three curses from the balcony, three old fairies happened by on the street below and heard everything.

In the evening, weary from their long trip, the fairies stopped at an inn. As soon as they were inside, one of them remarked, 'Just look at the wizard's daughter! She wouldn't be sleeping so soundly if she knew about her father's three curses!'

For there asleep on a bench in the inn were Pome, Peel, and the wizard's daughter. Peel wasn't actually asleep; perhaps he wasn't sleepy, or maybe he just considered it always wiser to sleep with one eye open and thus know what was going on around him.

So he overheard one fairy say, 'It's the wizard's will for her to come upon three horses – one white, one red, one black – and leap on the white one, which will be her undoing.'

'But,' put in the second fairy, 'if some far-seeing soul were present, he would cut off the horse's head at once, and nothing would happen.'

The third fairy added, 'Whoever breathes a word of this will turn to stone.'

'Then it's the wizard's will for her to come upon three pretty little dogs,' said the first fairy, 'and pick up the very one that will be her undoing.'

'But,' commented the second fairy, 'if some far-seeing soul were present, he would cut off the puppy's head at once, and nothing would happen.'

'Whoever breathes a word of this,' said the third fairy, 'will turn to stone.'

'It's finally his will, the first night she sleeps with her husband, for a giant snake to come through the window and destroy her.'

'But if some far-seeing soul were present, he would cut off the snake's head, and nothing would happen,' chimed in the second fairy.

'Whoever breathes a word of this will turn to stone.'

So Peel found himself in possession of three terrible secrets which he could not reveal without turning to stone.

14   The next morning they set out for a post house, where

Pome's father had three horses waiting for them – one white, one red, one black. The wizard's daughter immediately jumped into the saddle on the white one, but Peel promptly unsheathed his sword and cut off the horse's head.

'What are you doing? Have you lost your mind?'

'Forgive me, I am not at liberty to explain.'

'Pome, this Peel has a wicked heart!' said the wizard's daughter. 'I will travel no further in his company.'

But Peel admitted having cut off the horse's head in a moment of madness. He begged her to forgive him, which she ended up doing.

They reached the home of Pome's parents, and three pretty little dogs ran out to meet them – one white, one red, and one black. She bent down to pick up the black one, but Peel drew his sword and cut off the dog's head.

'Away with him at once, this crazy, cruel man!' screamed the bride.

At that moment Pome's parents came out. They heartily welcomed their son and his bride and, learning of the dispute with Peel, they persuaded her to pardon him once more. But at dinner, amidst the general merriment, Peel was pensive and aloof, nor could anyone make him say what was troubling him. 'Nothing's the matter, absolutely nothing,' he insisted, although he left the banquet early, under the pretext of being sleepy. But instead of going to his room, he entered the bridal chamber and hid under the bed.

The bride and bridegroom went to bed and fell asleep. Keeping watch, Peel soon heard the windowpane break, and in crawled a giant snake. Peel leaped out, bared his sword, and cut off the snake's head. At the commotion the bride awoke, saw Peel by the bed with his sword unsheathed, saw no snake (it had vanished), and screamed, 'Help! Murder! Peel wants to kill us! I've pardoned him two times already, let him be put to death this time!'

Peel was seized, imprisoned, and three days later dressed for the gallows. Imagining himself now doomed in any event, he asked permission to tell Pome's wife three things before dying. She came to him in prison.

'Do you remember,' Peel asked, 'when we stopped at an inn?'

'Of course I do.'

'Well, while you and your husband were sleeping, three fairies came in and said the wizard had placed three curses on his daughter: to come upon three horses and leap on the white horse, which would be her undoing. But, they added, should somebody quickly cut off the horse's head, nothing would happen. And whoever breathed a word of this would turn to stone.'

As he said those words, poor Peel's feet and legs turned to marble.

The young woman understood. 'That's enough, please!' she screamed. 'Don't tell me any more!'

But he went on: 'Doomed whether I speak or keep silent, I choose to speak. The three fairies also said the wizard's daughter would come upon three pretty little dogs . . .'

He related the curse regarding the little dogs and turned to stone up to his neck.

'I understand! Poor Peel, forgive me! Don't go on!' pleaded the bride.

But in a strained voice, since his throat was already marble, and stuttering, since his jaws were becoming marble, he told her about the curse with the snake. 'But . . . whoever breathes a word of this . . . will turn to stone . . .' At that, he was silent, marble from head to foot.

'What have I done!' moaned the young wife. 'This faithful soul is damned . . . unless . . . why, of course, the only person that can save him is my father.' And she took paper, pen, and ink, and wrote her father, asking his forgiveness and begging him to come to her.

The wizard, whose child was the apple of his eye, came to her at breakneck speed. 'Papa, dear,' she said as she kissed him, 'I am asking you a favor. Look at this poor youth. After saving my life and protecting me from your three curses, he has turned to stone from head to foot.'

Sighing, the wizard replied, 'For the love I bear you, I 17

will do this also.' He drew a phial of balsam from his pocket, brushed Peel with it, and Peel sprang back to life as sound as ever.

Thus, instead of leading him to the gallows, they bore him home in triumph, amid music and singing, while the throngs around him shouted, 'Long live Peel! Long live Peel!'

Spain was once ruled by the good and just King Maximilian. He had three sons: William, John, and little Andrew – the youngest and his father's favorite. Following an illness, the king lost his eyesight. Though all the doctors in the kingdom were summoned, none knew of any remedy. One of the oldest doctors suggested, 'Since medical knowledge is limited in this case, send for a soothsayer.' So soothsayers from everywhere were called in. They pored over their books, but proved no wiser than the doctors in the end. With the soothsayers a wizard had slipped in, a stranger to everyone. After the others had all had their say, the wizard came forward and spoke. 'I am familiar with cases of blindness like yours, King Maximilian. The cure is nowhere to be found but in the Sleeping Queen's city: it is the water in her well.' People's amazement at those words had not yet died down before the wizard vanished and was never heard of again.

The king was eager to find out who he was, but no one had ever laid eyes on the man before. One of the soothsayers thought he might be a wizard from the vicinity of Armenia, come to Spain by means of magic. The king asked, 'Could the Sleeping Queen's city also be there-abouts?' An old courtier replied, 'We won't know where it is until we look for it. If I were younger, I would go in search of it myself, without delay.'

William, the eldest son, stepped forward. 'If anyone is to set out in search of the city, I am the one to go. It is only fitting that the firstborn put his father's health above all other concerns.'

'Dear son,' replied the king, 'you have my blessing. Take money and horses and everything else you need. I will be expecting you back victorious in three months.'

William went to the kingdom's port and boarded a vessel sailing for the Isle of Buda, where it was to anchor for three hours before continuing on to Armenia. At Buda he went ashore to see the island. As he strolled about, he met a charming lady and became so engrossed in talking to her that the three hours went by before he knew it. At the appointed time the ship unfurled its sails and departed without William. He was sorry at first, but the lady's company made him soon forget all about his father's illness and the original purpose of the voyage.

When the three months were up, with still no sign of William, the king began fearing the boy was dead, and to the pain of going blind was added that of losing a son. To console him, John, the middle boy, volunteered to go in search of his brother as well as the water. The king consented, although fearful that something would happen to this son too.

On the boat, John soon came in sight of the Isle of Buda. This time the ship was to anchor there for a day. John went ashore to look around the island. He strolled into a park of myrtles, cypresses, and laurels, which shaded lagoons of limpid water stocked with fish of every color of the rainbow. From there he proceeded through the town's beautiful avenues and streets to a square with a white marble fountain in its center. Encircling the Square were monuments and buildings, and in their midst rose a majestic palace with gold and silver columns and crystal walls that sparkled in the sunlight. John spied his brother moving about on the other side of those crystal walls.

'William!' he cried. 'What are you doing here? Why did you not come home? We thought you were dead!' And they embraced.

William told how, once he'd set foot on the island, he'd been unable to tear himself away and how he'd been received by the beautiful lady who owned everything in sight. 'This lady is Lugistella,' he added, 'and she has a very lovely little sister named Isabel. If you like her, she is yours.'

In short, the twelve hours went by, and the ship sailed without John. After a brief spell of remorse, he too forgot 21 all about his father and the miraculous water and became a guest, like his brother, in the crystal palace.

When the three months were up, with no sign of the second son, King Maximilian was alarmed and, with the entire court, feared the worst. Then little Andrew boldly declared he would go in search of his brothers and the Sleeping Queen's magic water. 'So you intend to leave me too?' said the king. 'Blind and crushed as I am, I must give up my last son as well?' But Andrew revived his hope of seeing the three boys back safe and sound in addition to obtaining the wonderful water, so his father consented at last to his departure.

The ship dropped anchor at the Isle of Buda, where it would remain for two days. 'You may disembark,' the captain told Andrew, 'but be back on time if you don't want to be left behind like two other young men who went ashore and have not been heard of since.' Andrew realized he was talking of his brothers, who must be somewhere on the island. So he began looking around and found them in the crystal palace. They embraced, and the brothers told Andrew about the spell that kept them on Buda. 'We are in a real paradise here,' they told him. 'We each have a beautiful lady. The mistress of the island is mine, her sister is John's. If you'll join us, I believe our ladies still have a cousin . . .'

But Andrew cut them off. 'You've obviously lost your

mind if you don't remember your duty to Father! I intend to find the Sleeping Queen's magic water, and nothing can turn me from that resolution – neither riches, nor amusements, nor beautiful ladies!'

At those words, the brothers became silent and walked away in a huff. Andrew returned at once to the ship. The sails were unfurled, and favorable winds carried the vessel straight to Armenia.

As soon as he was on Armenian soil, Andrew asked everyone he met where the Sleeping Queen's city was, but apparently no one had ever heard of it. After weeks of vain search, he was directed to an old man living on a mountaintop. 'He's an old, old man, as old as the world itself, by the name of Farfanello. If he doesn't know where this city is, nobody knows.'

Andrew climbed the mountain. He found the bearded, decrepit old man in his hut and told him what he was seeking. 'Dear youth,' said Farfanello, 'I have indeed heard of this place, but it is quite far away. First you have to cross an ocean, and that will take almost a month, to say nothing of the perils of sailing those waters. But even if you do get across them safe and sound, still greater dangers lie in store for you on the Sleeping Queen's isle, the very name of which suggests misfortune, since they call it the Isle of Tears.'

Glad to have definite information at last, Andrew 23

embarked at the port of Brindisse. The ocean crossing was hazardous because huge polar bears, capable of wrecking even big ships, swam in those waters. But Andrew, a courageous hunter, was not afraid, and the vessel steered clear of the polar bears' claws and arrived at the Isle of Tears. The port looked abandoned, and not a sound was to be heard. Andrew disembarked and saw a sentinel holding a gun, but the man was completely motionless. Even though Andrew asked him for directions, he continued to stand as still and silent as a statue. Next, Andrew approached the porters about his baggage, but they didn't move a muscle; some held heavy trunks on their backs, with one foot forward and raised. Andrew entered the city. On one side of the street he saw a cobbler, still and silent, halted in the midst of drawing thread through a shoe. On the other side of the street a coffeehouse keeper held a pot in position to pour a lady a cup of coffee, but both he and she were mute and motionless. Streets, windows, and shops were full of people, but they all looked like figures of wax in the strangest of postures. Even the horses, dogs, cats, and other creatures were standing dead still in their tracks. Moving through this thick silence, Andrew came to a splendid palace adorned with statues and tablets commemorating the island's past kings: on the façade was a frieze full of figures, with an inscription in radiant letters of gold: TO HER MAJESTY THE QUEEN OF

LUMINOUS SOULS, WHO REIGNS OVER THIS ISLE OF PARIMUS.

'Where could this queen be?' wondered Andrew. 'Could she be one and the same as the Sleeping Queen?' He went up a grand alabaster staircase and crossed several halls decorated with bas-reliefs and guarded at the doors by the customary men of arms, over whom a spell had been cast. In one hall marble steps led up to a dais, on which stood the throne surmounted by a canopy and displaying a diamond-studded coat-of-arms. A grapevine growing in a gold pot had trailed clear across the room and twined around the throne and canopy, adorning them with clusters of ripe grapes and vine leaves. That wasn't all: fruit trees of every kind in the garden had grown quite out of bounds, thrusting their branches through the windows into the hall. Andrew, who was hungry after so much walking, pulled an apple from one of those branches and bit into it. He'd no sooner done so than his eyesight dimmed, then left him altogether. 'Woe is me!' he cried. 'How will I now get about in this strange country peopled with nothing but statues?' He began groping his way out of the palace; but moving along, he suddenly stepped into a hole and plummeted through empty space, landing in water over his head. With a few strokes he came to the surface, and the minute his head was out of water, he realized he had regained his eyesight. He was at the bottom of a deep well, and high above him was the sky. 'So this is the well,' he said to himself, 'the wizard was referring to. This is the water that will cure my father, if I ever manage to get out of here and carry some back to him.' He spied a rope hanging in the well, took hold of it, and climbed out.

It was nighttime, so Andrew looked about for a bed to sleep in. He found a bedchamber royally decorated and containing a large bed, in which a maiden of angelic beauty lay sleeping. The maiden's eyes were closed and her face was peaceful, so Andrew knew she had been put under a spell while she slept. After a little reflection, he undressed and slipped into bed beside her passing a delightful night without her giving any sign she knew he was there. At daybreak he jumped out of bed and wrote her a note, which he left on her bedside table: 'To his great joy, Andrew, son of King Maximilian of Spain, slept in this bed on the 21st of March, in the year 203.' He filled a bottle with the water that restored eyesight and plucked one of the apples that caused blindness, and set out for home.

The ship again called at the port of Buda, where Andrew stopped to visit his brothers. He told them of the wonders of the Isle of Tears and the night he had spent with the lovely maiden. Then he showed them the apple which took away one's eyesight and the water which restored it. Possessed with sudden envy, the two brothers hatched a plot against Andrew. They stole the bottle of magic water, leaving in its place one exactly like it. Then they informed him they would accompany him home in order to present their wives to their father.

No words can describe the joy of King Maximilian at the safe return of all three of his sons to Spain. After many hearty embraces, the king asked, 'Which one of you was the luckiest?' William and John held their tongues, but Andrew spoke up. 'Father, I make bold to say I was, for I found and brought back my lost brothers. I reached the Sleeping Queen's city and got the water that will restore your eyesight. I also got something else amazing, and I'm going to show you right this minute how it works.'

He pulled out the apple and handed it to his mother to eat. The queen bit into it, went blind on the instant, and let out a scream. 'Don't get upset, Mamma,' said Andrew, taking out the bottle, 'for a drop of this water will restore your sight and also that of Papa, who's been blind for so long.'

But the water came from the bottle substituted by the older brothers, so she did not regain her sight. The queen wept, the king raged, and Andrew trembled in his boots. Then the two brothers came forward and said, 'This has happened because he didn't find the Sleeping Queen's magic water. We found it ourselves, and here it is.' Once the stolen water had touched their eyes, the two old people could see again as well as ever.

A big row followed. Andrew called his brothers thieves and traitors, and they turned around and called him a little liar. The king could make neither head nor tail of the dispute, but finally he sided with William and John and their wives, and said to Andrew, 'Silence, you shameless wretch! You not only had no intention of curing me, but you meant to blind your mother as well! Guards, away with this ungrateful creature! Take him to the woods and slay him! And bring me back his heart, or more heads will roll!'

The soldiers dragged out Andrew, screaming and protesting, to a thicket outside the city. But Andrew managed to tell his story and convince them. So as to avoid staining their hands with innocent blood, the soldiers made him promise never to come back to town, then set him free. They returned to the king with the heart of a pig purchased from a farmer and slaughtered on the spot.

On the Isle of Tears nine months went by, and the sleeping maiden gave birth to a fine baby boy. As she brought him forth, she awakened. With the Queen now awake, the spell was broken which Morgan le Fay had cast 28 over her out of envy, and the whole city awakened and came back to life. The soldiers frozen at attention relaxed, those at ease jumped to attention, the cobbler finished drawing the thread through the shoe, the coffeehouse keeper overfilled the lady's cup, and the porters at the port shifted their loads to the other shoulder, since the first shoulder was a bit weary by now.

The queen rubbed her eyes and said, 'I wonder who on earth was so bold as to make his way to the island and sleep in this room and thereby free me and my dear subjects from the spell we were under.'

One of her maids of honor then handed her the note from the night table, so the queen knew her visitor had been Andrew, son of King Maximilian. Right away she wrote the king to send Andrew to her without delay, or else she would make war on Spain.

When King Maximilian got that letter, he called in William and John to read it and give their opinion. Neither one of them knew what to say. At last, William spoke. 'We'll never know what this is all about unless somebody goes to the queen for an explanation. I'll go myself and see what I can find out.'

William's trip was easier, since Morgan le Fay's spell had been broken and all the polar bears had disappeared. He went before the queen, saying he was Prince Andrew.

The queen, who was naturally distrustful, began to question him. 'What day did you come here the first time?

How did you find the city? Where was I? What happened to you in the palace? What do you see now that you didn't see before?' And on and on. William soon got all confused and started stammering, so the queen knew right away he was lying. She had his head chopped off and stuck on a spike atop the city gate, with the inscription: IF YOU LIE, THIS IS HOW YOU WILL DIE.

King Maximilian got a second letter from the sometime Sleeping Queen saying if he didn't send Andrew to her, troops were ready to move against him and reduce his kingdom, his people, his family, and himself to ashes. Long regretful of having ordered Andrew slain, the king wailed to John, 'Now what do we do? How will we tell her that Andrew is dead? And why doesn't William come home?' John volunteered to go to the sometime Sleeping Queen himself. He reached the island, but the sight of William's head on the city gate told him all he needed to know, and he returned home at full speed. 'Father!' he exclaimed, 'we are done for! William is dead, and his head is on a spike atop the city gate. If I had gone in, there would have been another head next to it.'

The king was beside himself with grief. 'William dead? Also William! Now I know for sure Andrew was innocent, and all this has happened to punish me. Tell me the truth, John; confess your treachery before I die.'

'Our wives are to blame!' said John. 'We never went to

the Sleeping Queen ourselves, and we put a bottle of ordinary water in the place of Andrew's magic liquid.'

Railing, weeping, and pulling out his hair, the king summoned the soldiers to take him to the spot where Andrew was buried. Among the soldiers this order caused great alarm. The king noticed it and was filled with new hope. 'Out with it! I want the truth. Whatever it is you're guilty of, I give you my royal word that you are pardoned.'

Trembling in their boots, the soldiers admitted that they had flatly disobeyed the order to slay Andrew. To their great surprise, the king began madly hugging and kissing them. Posted at every street corner was an announcement that whoever found Andrew would be richly rewarded for the rest of his life.

Andrew returned, to the infinite joy of his old father and the court, and set out at once for the Isle of Tears where he was given a hero's welcome.

'Andrew, who freed me and my people,' said the queen, 'you will be my husband and king forever!' For months afterward, all you heard on the island were songs of joy, so they called it the Isle of Happiness.

The Enchanted Palace

A king of long ago had a son named Fiordinando who never took his nose out of his books. He was always shut up in his room reading. From time to time he would close the book and gaze out the window at the garden and the woods beyond, then resume his reading and musing. Never did he leave his room except for lunch or dinner, or maybe for a rare stroll in the garden.

One day the king's hunter, a bright young man who as a child had played with the prince, said to the king, 'May I call on Fiordinando, Majesty? I've not seen him for quite some time.'

The king replied, 'By all means. Your visit will be a pleasant diversion for my fine son.'

So the hunter entered the room of Fiordinando, who looked him over and asked, 'What brings you to the court in those hobnailed boots?'

'I am the king's hunter,' explained the young man, who went on to describe the many kinds of game, the ways of birds and hares, and the different parts of the woods.

Fiordinando's imagination was kindled. 'Listen,' he said to the youth, 'I too shall try my luck at hunting. But don't say anything to my father, so he won't think it was your idea. I'll simply ask him to let me go hunting with you one morning.'

'At your service, as always,' replied the young man.

The next day at breakfast, Fiordinando said to the king, 'Yesterday I read a book on hunting which was so interesting I'm dying to go out and try my luck. May I?'

'Hunting is a dangerous sport,' replied the king, 'for someone who is new to it. But I won't keep you from something you think you might like. For a companion I'll let you have my hunter, who is unequaled as a hunting dog. Don't ever let him out of your sight.'

Next morning at sunrise Fiordinando and the hunter mounted their horses with their guns on shoulder straps and off to the woods they galloped. The hunter aimed at every bird or hare he saw and laid it low. Fiordinando tried his best to keep pace, but missed everything he shot at. At the end of the day the hunter's game bag was bulging, whereas Fiordinando hadn't brought down so much as one feather. At dusk Fiordinando spied a small hare hiding under a bush and took aim. But it was so small and frightened he decided he would simply run up and grab it. Just as he reached the bush, the hare darted off, with Fiordinando close behind. Every time he was right upon it, the hare would run far ahead, then stop, as though it were waiting for Fiordinando to catch up, only to elude him again. In the meantime Fiordinando had strayed so far from the hunter that he could no longer find the way back. Again and again he called out, but no one answered. By now it was completely dark, and the hare had disappeared.

Weary and distressed, Fiordinando sat down under a tree to rest. It was not long before he saw what seemed to be a light shining through the trees. He therefore got up, made his way through the underbrush, and emerged in a vast clearing, at the end of which stood the most ornate of palaces.

The front door was open, and Fiordinando called out, 'Hello! Is anyone at home?' He was answered with dead silence; not even an echo came back to him. Entering, he found a large hall with a fire burning in the fireplace and, nearby, wine and glasses. Fiordinando took a seat to rest and warm up and drink a little wine. Then he rose and passed into another room where a table was set for two persons. The cutlery, plates, and goblets were gold and silver; the curtains, tablecloth, and napkins were pure silk embroidered with pearls and diamonds; from the ceiling hung lamps of solid gold the size of baskets. Since no one was there and he was hungry, Fiordinando sat down to the table.

He had scarcely eaten his first mouthful when he heard a rustle of dresses coming down the steps, and in walked a queen followed by twelve maids of honor. The queen was young and extremely beautiful of figure, but her face was hidden by a heavy veil. Neither she nor the twelve maids of honor said one word during the entire meal. She sat across the table in silence from Fiordinando while the maids quietly served them and poured their wine. The meal thus passed in silence, and the queen carried her food to her mouth under that thick veil. When they had finished, the queen rose, and the maids of honor accompanied her back upstairs. Fiordinando also rose and continued his tour of the palace.

Coming to a master bedchamber with a bed all turned down for the night, he undressed and jumped under the covers. Behind the canopy was a secret door: it opened, and in walked the queen, still mute, veiled, and followed by her twelve maids of honor. With Fiordinando leaning on his elbow and gaping, the maids of honor undressed the queen all but for her veil, put her in bed beside Fiordinando, and left the room. Fiordinando was sure she would say something now or unveil her face. But she had already fallen asleep. He watched the veil rising and falling with her breath, thought about it a minute, then he too fell asleep.

At dawn the maids of honor returned, put the queen's clothes back on her, and led her away. Fiordinando also got up, ate the hearty breakfast he found waiting for him, and went down to the stables.

His horse was there eating oats. Fiordinando climbed into the saddle and galloped off to the woods. The whole day long he looked for a road that would take him back home, or for some trace of his hunting companion, but he only got lost anew, and when night fell, there stood the clearing and palace once more.

He went inside, and the same things happened as the evening before. But the next day as he was galloping through the woods he met the hunter, who'd been looking for him for the last three days, and together they returned to the city. When the hunter questioned him, Fiordinando made up a tale about a lot of complicated mishaps, but said nothing about what had really happened.

Back at the royal palace Fiordinando was like a changed person. His eyes wandered constantly from the pages of his book to the woods beyond the garden. Seeing him so moody, listless, and absorbed, his mother began pestering him to tell her what he was brooding over. She kept nagging until Fiordinando finally told her from beginning to end what had happened to him in the woods. He made no bones about being in love with the beautiful queen and wondering how to marry her when she neither spoke nor showed her face.

'I'll tell you what to do,' replied his mother. 'Sup with her one more time. When the two of you are seated, accidentally knock her fork off the table. When she bends 37 over to pick it up, pull off her veil. You can be sure she'll say something then.'

No sooner had he received that advice than Fiordinando saddled his horse and raced off to the palace in the woods, where he was welcomed in the usual manner. At supper he knocked the queen's fork off the table with his elbow. She bent over, and he tore off her veil. At that, the queen rose, as beautiful as a moonbeam and as fiery as a ray of sun. 'Rash youth!' she screamed. 'You have betrayed me. Had I been able to sleep one more night beside you without speaking or unveiling my face, I would have been free from the spell and you would have become my husband. Now I'll have to go off to Paris for a week and from there to Peterborough, where I'll given in prize at a tournament, and heaven knows who will win me. Farewell! And note that I am the queen of Portugal!'

In the same instant she vanished, along with the entire palace, and Fiordinando found himself alone and abandoned in the thickest part of the underbrush. It was no easy task to find his way home, but once he got there, he didn't waste a minute. He filled a purse with money, summoned his faithful hunter, and departed on horseback for Paris. They wore themselves out riding, but didn't dismount until they reached an inn in that famous city.

Nor did he spend long resting up, for he wished to

learn if the queen of Portugal really was there in Paris. He began pumping the innkeeper. 'What's the news around here?'

The innkeeper replied, 'None to speak of. What sort of news do you expect?'

'There's all kind of news,' replied Fiordinando. 'News about wars, feast days, famous people passing through the city . . .'

'Oh!' exclaimed the innkeeper, 'come to think about it, there is a piece of interesting news: five days ago the queen of Portugal arrived in Paris. In three more days she'll leave for Peterborough. She's a very beautiful lady and highly educated. She enjoys exploring unusual spots, and strolls outside the city gate near here every afternoon with twelve maids of honor.'

'And it's possible to get a look at her?' asked Fiordinando.

'Why not? When she walks in public, any passer-by can see her.'

'Wonderful!' said Fiordinando. 'In the meantime get dinner for us and serve it with a bottle of red wine.'

Now the innkeeper had a daughter who rejected all wooers, mind you, because none of them suited her. But the instant she laid eyes on Fiordinando getting out of his saddle, she told herself he would be the only one she would ever consider. She went to her father at once to say she had fallen in love and to ask him to find a way for her to marry the stranger. So the innkeeper said to Fiordinando, 'I hope you'll like Paris and have the good fortune to find yourself a lovely bride here.'

'My bride,' replied Fiordinando, 'is the most beautiful queen in the world, and I am trailing her all over the globe.'

The innkeeper's daughter, who was eavesdropping, was seized with rage. When her father sent her to the cellar after the wine, she thrust a handful of opium into the bottle. Fiordinando and the hunter went outside the city after dinner to await the queen of Portugal, but suddenly they became so drowsy that they sank to the ground and slept like logs. Shortly thereafter the queen came by, recognized Fiordinando, bent over him, called his name, caressed him, shook him, and rolled him over and over; but there was no waking him. Then she slipped a diamond ring from her finger and placed it on his brow.

Now in a cave nearby lived a hermit who had witnessed the whole scene from behind a tree. As soon as the queen left, he tiptoed out, picked up the ring from Fiordinando's brow, and retreated with it to his cave.

When Fiordinando awakened, it was already dark, and it took him a while to recall where he was. He shook the hunter awake, and together they cursed the red wine for being too strong and lamented over missing the queen.

The second day they said to the innkeeper, 'Give us white wine, but make sure it's not too strong.' The daughter, however, drugged the white wine too, and the young men went back only to end up snoring in the middle of the meadow.

At a loss to awaken Fiordinando, the queen of Portugal placed a lock of her hair on his brow and fled. The hermit emerged from the grove of trees and made off with the lock. When Fiordinando and the hunter awakened in the middle of the night, they had no idea what had taken place.

Fiordinando became suspicious of the sleep that came over him every afternoon. It was now the last day before the queen would be leaving for Peterborough, and he intended to see her at all costs. He thus told the innkeeper to bring him no more wine. But the daughter now drugged the soup. So, upon arriving in the meadow, Fiordinando felt his head drooping already. He pulled out two pistols and showed them to the hunter. 'I know you're loyal,' he said, 'but I warn you that if you don't stay awake today and keep me awake, you are going to get it. I'll unload both of these into your head, and I don't mean maybe.'

At that, Fiordinando stretched out and began to snore. To stay awake, the hunter tried pinching himself repeatedly, but between one pinch and the next his eyes would close, and the pinches became rarer and rarer, until he too was snoring.

The queen arrived. With cries, embraces, slaps in the face, kisses, and shakes, she did her best to awaken Fiordinando. But realizing she would not succeed, she began weeping so violently that instead of tears a few drops of blood trickled down her cheeks. She wiped the blood off with her handkerchief, which she placed over Fiordinando's face. Then she got back into her carriage and sped straight to Peterborough. Meanwhile the hermit came out of the cave, picked up the handkerchief, and stood by to see exactly what would happen.

When Fiordinando woke up at night and realized he'd missed his last chance to see the queen, he was fit to be tied. He pulled out the pistols and was about to carry out his threat of unloading them in the sleeping hunter's head, when the hermit grabbed him by the wrists and said, 'That poor fellow is blameless. The culprit is the inn-keeper's daughter who drugged the red wine, the white wine, and the soup.'

'Why would she do a thing like that?' asked Fiordinando. 'And how do you know so much about it?'

'She's in love with you and gave you opium. I know all about it from peeping through the trees at everything that goes on here. For the last three days the queen of Portugal has come by and tried to awaken you, leaving on your brow a diamond, a lock of her hair, and a handkerchief moist with tears of blood.'

'And where are these things now?'

'I took them away for safekeeping, since there are many thieves around here who would have stolen them before you ever got to see them. Here they are. Look after them, because if you act sensibly, they will bring you luck.'

'What am I to do?'

'The queen of Portugal,' explained the hermit, 'has gone to Peterborough where she will be given in prize at a tournament. The knight who jousts with this ring, this lock of hair, and this handkerchief on the tip of his lance will be invincible and wed the queen.'

Fiordinando didn't have to be told twice. He sped from Paris to Peterborough, where he arrived in time to enter the list of jousters, but under a false name. Illustrious warriors had arrived from all over the world with wagon-loads of luggage, servants, and arms as shiny as the sun. In the heart of the city a large arena had been surrounded with viewing stands, and there the knights were to contend on horseback for the queen of Portugal.

With his visor lowered, Fiordinando won the first day, thanks to the diamond on the tip of his lance. He won the second day with the lock of hair. He won the third with the handkerchief. Horses and men fell by the dozens until not a one was left standing. Fiordinando was proclaimed victor and the queen's bridegroom. Only then did he open his helmet. The queen recognized him and swooned for joy.

There was a grand wedding, and Fiordinando sent for his mother and father, who had already given him up for dead and gone into mourning. He introduced his bride to them, saying, 'This is none other than the little hare I pursued, the veiled lady, and the queen of Portugal whom I have freed from an awful spell.'

The King of Portugal's Son

The king of Portugal had a son named Peter, who was dying to get married if only he could find a girl that suited him. On his way home from hunting one day, Peter spied on a shoemaker's doorstep a very beautiful girl with thick golden hair, sparkling brown eyes, and rosy cheeks. 'She is certainly beautiful enough to be my wife,' said Peter to himself. He got to the palace, put his gun up, changed into clothing appropriate to his rank, then went back out. 'Come what may, I'm going to have a little chat with her,' he told himself. 'It's a shame she's only a shoemaker's daughter!' Thinking such thoughts, he reached the shop, struck up a conversation, and found the girl to be not only beautiful but also quite refined. In short, he fell head over heels in love with her and asked: 'Will you have me for your spouse?'

'What!' she laughed. 'You're joking! You are a king's son, and I'm the daughter of a poor shoemaker. We've nothing in common.'

'I'm serious,' replied Peter. 'I want you, and I don't care who your father is. If you like me, I will marry you.' 45

To make a long story short, they became engaged and, walking on air, Peter returned to the palace, as it was now dinner time.

At table he passed up the soup, then the main dish, and when they came to dessert, he said, 'Father, I've decided to get married, and I've found my bride.'

The king was overjoyed at first, but upon learning who the girl was, he exclaimed, 'What! A shoemaker's daughter? That's no bride fit for a king. What would the nobility say? What would all the people say when they saw a shoemaker's daughter on the throne of Portugal? No, a thousand times no, this wedding cannot take place.'

'Father,' answered Peter, 'I'm sorry you're unhappy about it, but I gave the girl my word, my royal word. So you see I've no choice now but to wed her.'

'That being the case,' said the king in dismay, 'keep your promise, by all means. But outside this palace and this kingdom. Here, I want to see neither you nor her.'

The ceremony took place in a few days, but without pomp, and then the newlyweds and one maid climbed into a coach and headed for Paris. When it was night, Peter, his bride, and the maid, worn out from the day's journey, went sound asleep in the coach while the drivers whipped the horses onward. It was so dark that, upon arriving at a crossroads, the drivers made a slip and, instead of going to the right, took the road to the left into a dense forest and immediately lost their way. All of a sudden, out rushed a herd of wild beasts, which attacked horses and drivers and devoured them all in a flash. At the uproar, Peter awakened and called the drivers, but there was, naturally, no answer, as they were dead. He climbed out of the coach, and there on the ground lay only the boots of those unfortunate men and the hoofs of the horses. Frightened, the women also left the coach and, in an attempt to get out of the forest, the three of them ran until they came to a clearing, where they dropped from exhaustion. Peter threw up a shelter of branches, in which they rested for the remainder of the night, half dead from fear and running.

At dawn Peter got up before the others and went outside. Some distance away was a fountain, so he picked up his gun, which he always carried with him, and went to wash. Reaching the fountain, he removed his hat and placed his diamond ring on it, so he could wash his hands and face. But as he rinsed, a little bird swooped down, picked up the ring, and flew into a tree with it. Peter grabbed his gun and ran after the bird; but when he took aim, the bird flew to another tree, with the king's son running after it. Peter thus spent the entire day running from tree to tree, without managing to shoot the bird. Night fell, and the little bird went to roost, but it was now too dark for Peter to see a thing. As he hated to lose his ring, he decided to spend the night under the tree and shoot the bird at daybreak. He was actually up before dawn, with his gun aimed at the roost, but the little bird outsmarted him and got away again. What with the bird flying and Peter running, they went quite far away and came to a very high wall, over which the bird disappeared.

It was a thick wall without doors or windows. Peter decided to skirt it and, before too long, found himself in the heart of the woods. There he saw a tree so tall that one of its limbs extended over the wall, so Peter climbed to the top and took a look. On the other side of the wall was a beautiful garden, in which he saw the bird calmly pecking. Peter slid from the branch to the top of the wall, then jumped safely into the garden. With his gun aimed, he crept up on the bird, but this time too it got away, flying over the wall and disappearing into the woods. Peter was now a prisoner in the garden. He tried to scale the wall, but there was no possible way to escape.

In the thick of Peter's struggle, a sorcerer appeared. His eyes blazed as he yelled, 'Rogue! Thief! I've caught you at last. Now I know who's been pulling up my plants!'

'No, indeed, sir,' answered Peter. 'There's surely a mistake. I slipped in here for an entirely different reason, and nothing was further from my mind than destroying or stealing anything of yours.'

But the sorcerer refused to listen to reason, and his eyes

gleamed with rage: he was bent on putting Peter to death. Seeing himself in a hopeless predicament, Peter fell to his knees and begged the sorcerer not to kill him, telling in detail what had befallen him.

'Very well,' replied the sorcerer, 'in time I'll see whether or not you're telling the truth. Meanwhile, come with me into my palace.'

They went into the palace, where they found the sorceress, wife of the sorcerer. 'What's new, my husband?' she asked.

'I found this young man tearing up our beautiful garden. What shall we do with him?'

After hearing the whole story, the sorceress said, 'Well, if he's told the truth, we must spare him. Let's test him, husband, to see whether he's a liar or not, and whether he's good for something or good for nothing. Afterward we'll decide what to do with him.'

So Peter was put to work in the large garden looking after the flowers and vegetables. He took pains to satisfy the two sorcerers and obey them at all times. The sorcerers were delighted over how beautifully he kept the garden and, all in all, looked on him as their very own son.

Several months went by, and one day the sorcerer said, 'Listen, Peter, you are now to dig up this little field here, because I shall sow it in a particular manner of my own.' Peter set to work digging, and what should he see as he bent over but the little bird with the ring, which flew right down to the worked ground and began scratching around in it! Peter didn't hesitate a minute, but ran for his gun, aimed, fired and, this time, brought the bird down dead. He touched its crop and felt the ring still there.

At the blast, the sorcerer had come running. 'What happened? What happened?' he cried.

'Look, Uncle' – he now called the sorcerer – 'here's the clear proof I'm a nobleman, and that I was telling the truth the first time I set foot in your splendid garden. You remember my telling you about the little bird and the ring? Well, I've killed the bird at last, and the ring is still in its crop.'

'This means,' replied the sorcerer, 'that you can consider yourself as my true son and just as much the owner of everything here as I am.'

So Peter lived there as the son of the sorcerer and the sorceress, but he disliked being forever cooped up in that garden and constantly hinted he would like nothing better than to leave. The sorcerer, who truly loved him like a son, realizing what he wanted, said, 'Listen, to go outside this wall is quite dangerous, for the surrounding woods are full of wild animals. I'll never understand how you got here without being eaten alive. But if you wait for the day when there's a storm at sea, you will see the water rise to the top of the wall and ships arrive and moor to those spires up there on the roof. If you are patient, you will be able to sail away on one of those ships.'

Several months went by before the sorcerer finally announced, 'Tomorrow there will be a storm at sea, Peter. If you still want to leave, get ready. I hate to see you go, but do as you will. However, first go into the treasure storeroom and take as much money as you like.'

Peter didn't have to be begged. He went down into the treasury and filled his pockets with beautiful coins.

The next morning when he got up, he saw that the sorcerer had spoken the truth: the sea was on a level with the top of the wall, with the ships moored up at the battlements. Peter went to one of the ships and asked, 'Captain, what is your destination?'

'I'm bound for the port of Spain.'

'Fine! I too will sail for Spain if you'll take me aboard.'

He bid the sorcerer and sorceress farewell, thanking them for the kindness they had shown him, went aboard the ship, and landed in Spain a few days later and went to an inn. He had no idea what he had come to the port of Spain to do, so he asked the servant at the inn, 'Is there any way to get work here in the city?'

'Why not? There's a man whose job is precisely to find jobs for people, and he comes by here every morning.'

When the man showed up, Peter went to him and was 51

told, 'If you're interested, the governor is looking for a footman.'

Peter said he was interested, the man took him to the governor, and Peter became his confidential servant. Every day he took his master's children to school. Now the master used to give the children a pocketful of coins so that they would learn to practice charity in the street. To whoever asked in God's name, they gave a penny. And everybody who got a penny from the children would then receive five pence from Peter, who had all that money given him by the sorcerer.

Word of this instantly spread all over the city, and the people began grumbling about the governor, saying, 'The footman would make a far better governor than the old skinflint who presently governs.' A great tumult arose: the people went and shouted under the governor's windows, 'Down with him! Down with the governor! We want Peter the footman for our governor!'

But Peter went to the window and signaled for the people to behave, at which they grew calm and left.

Now the governor had a marriageable daughter who was in love with Peter. When she saw that the people wanted him in her father's place, she made such a fuss that the governor had to let her marry Peter. In the meantime Peter continued his almsgiving, only now, instead of five pence, he gave ten. A still greater tumult resulted than before, and the governor thought it wiser to withdraw to one of his country villas. Peter took his place and governed so well that everyone without exception was delighted.

Let's go back a bit, to the wife and maid Peter had left in the shelter of branches when the bird flew off with his ring. Finding Peter gone, the two women went everywhere looking for him and thus passed through many cities and towns. After months and months of travel, they too ended up in the port of Spain. They took lodgings in an inn, had a hairdresser cut their hair short and a tailor made them men's clothing, and asked the servant at the inn if there was work to be had in some house or other.

'There's a man,' explained the servant, 'who looks for servants in particular for the rich. Speak to him of the matter.'

The man arrived, spoke with the two women, and said, 'It just so happens our new governor needs a cook and a footman. I'll take you both to him.'

They came to terms, and the shoemaker's daughter took the job of cook, while her maid became the footman. But so much time had passed that Peter did not recognize them, nor did they recognize Peter.

Not many days later Peter said to his wife, the governor's daughter, 'I won't be home for dinner today. Certain

noblemen have invited me out, so I'll leave you by
yourself.'

'By all means, go,' replied his wife. 'Rather than stay
here by myself and be bored, I'll go to Papa's villa and
keep him company awhile. I'll even stay for a few days.'
So they each went their own way.

Remaining behind at the palace were the cook and the
footman – that is, the two women in disguise. The cook
said, 'I'm going to give the kitchen a thorough cleaning
while the master and mistress are away. Hold on to this
ring my husband gave me when we became engaged, as I
don't want to damage it.'

The footman took the ring and slipped it on, so as
not to lose it. Then he went to put the master bedchamber in order, and to avoid scratching the ring, he removed it and placed it on the chest of drawers. But
once he had finished, he forgot to put the ring back on
his finger.

In the evening Peter returned, dined in high spirits,
then went to bed. The next morning as soon as he opened
his eyes he saw the ring sparkling on top of the chest of
drawers. 'Whose ring is this?' he wondered, picking it up
and examining it from every angle. He had a strong
feeling he had seen it before. He rang the bell and asked
the footman who put the ring there.

'Oh, please excuse me, sir,' replied the footman, 'I'm all

to blame. I forgot and left the ring there myself. It's not mine, though; it belongs to the cook.'

'Send the cook to me, then,' said Peter, and the cook came up too.

To make a long story short, what with questions, answers, and explanations, they all ended up recognizing each other. But if the women were excited, Peter was far less so, for he was thinking of his other wife there in Spain, and had no idea how to get out of such a mess. When the governor's daughter returned from the country, Peter took heart and told her of his past and how his first wife had turned up there at the palace. 'Tell me now how to get out of this,' he concluded, 'for I frankly don't know what to do.'

His second wife answered, as though nothing were amiss. 'Is that all that's bothering you? Do you think I'm jealous? Even if you have two wives instead of one, so what? The Turks have as many as twelve.'

Peter couldn't believe his ears. Was it possible to live with two wives who were not at one another's throats?

At nightfall, Peter said, 'Well, who is going to sleep with me tonight?'

The governor's daughter replied, 'It's only fair for your first wife to, after all this time apart.'

So Peter went off to bed with his first wife. But not an hour had gone by when the door opened and the governor's daughter entered with a pistol in each hand. One bullet in Peter's head, one bullet in his wife's head, and the jealous and false-hearted woman was revenged.

At the noise the whole palace woke up and, running into Peter's room, beheld that awful scene. The guard immediately seized the governor's daughter, who was led to the square next morning into the throng of outraged citizens, fastened to a pyre, coated with pitch, and burned alive for the crime she had committed.

Apple Girl

There was once a king and a queen who were very sad because they had no children. The queen kept asking, 'Why can't I bear children the same as the apple tree bears apples?'

Now it happened that instead of bearing a son, the queen gave birth to an apple, but an apple redder and more beautiful than any you ever saw. The king placed it on a gold tray on his balcony.

Across the street from the king lived a second king who happened to be standing at his window one day and saw, on his neighbor's balcony, a beautiful maiden as fair and rosy as an apple bathing and combing her hair in the sun. Open-mouthed, he stood staring at her, never having seen so lovely a maiden. But the minute the girl realized she was being observed, she ran back to the tray and disappeared inside the apple. The king had fallen madly in love with her.

He racked his brains and ended up crossing the street and knocking on the door, which the queen answered. 'Majesty,' he said to her, 'I have a favor to ask of you.'

'By all means, Majesty,' replied the queen. 'Any way neighbors can help one another out . . .'

'I would like to have that magnificent apple on your balcony.'

'Do you know what you're asking, Majesty? I'm that apple's mother, mind you, and I had to wait a long time before I had her.'

But the king wouldn't take no for an answer, so the other king and queen had to grant his wish, in order for them all to remain good neighbors. Thus he went home with the apple, which he took straight to his own room. He put out everything necessary for her toilette, and the maiden would emerge every morning to bathe and arrange her hair while he looked on. That was all she did. She neither ate nor talked; she only bathed and arranged her hair, then went back inside the apple.

The king lived with his stepmother, whose suspicions were aroused by her stepson's constant seclusion in his room. 'I'd give anything to know what my son is up to!'

War broke out, and the king had to go off and fight. It broke his heart to leave his apple. He called his most trusted servant to him and said, 'I'm leaving the key to my room with you. See that nobody goes in. Put out water and a comb every day for the apple girl, and make sure she has everything she needs. And don't forget, she tells me everything.' (That wasn't so, the girl never said a word, but the king thought it wise to tell his servant the contrary.) 'If a hair of her head is harmed during my absence, you'll pay with your life.'

'Have no fear, Majesty, I will look after her to the very best of my ability.'

As soon as the king was gone, the stepmother queen went to all lengths to get into his room. She put opium into the wine of his servant and stole the key from him when he fell asleep. She unlocked the door and turned the room upside down in search of clues to her stepson's strange behavior; but the more she searched, the less she found. The only thing out of the ordinary in the room was that splendid apple in a golden fruit bowl. 'It must be this apple that is always on his mind!'

Queens, as you well know, always have a small dagger concealed in their sashes. She took out her dagger and began pricking the apple all over. Out of every wound flowed a rivulet of blood. The stepmother queen grew frightened, ran away, and replaced the key in the sleeping servant's pocket.

When the servant awakened, he had no idea what had happened to him. He ran into the king's room and found blood all over the place. 'Oh, my goodness, what will I do now?' he exclaimed and fled.

He went to an aunt of his who was a fairy and possessed all the magic powders. The aunt took a powder suitable for apples under spells and another for bewitched maidens, and blended them.

The servant returned to the apple and sprinkled all the wounds with the mixture. The apple burst open, and out stepped the maiden in bandages and plaster casts.

The king came home, and for the first time, the maiden spoke. 'Would you believe that your stepmother stabbed me all over with her dagger? But your servant has nursed me back to health. I am eighteen and was under a spell. If you like, I will be your bride.'

'If I like! Indeed I do!'

The wedding was celebrated, to the great joy of both palaces. The only person missing was the stepmother, who fled and was never heard of again.

> Merrily through life they went,
> But were only content
> To give me one cent
> I never spent.

Joseph Ciufolo, Tiller-flutist

There was once a youth named Joseph Ciufolo, who played the flute when he wasn't tilling the soil. One day he was dancing through the fields and playing his flute to relax awhile from all his digging, when he suddenly spied a corpse lying on the ground beneath a swarm of flies. He put down his flute, walked up to the body, shooed the flies away, and covered the dead man with green boughs. Returning to the spot where he had left his hoe, he saw that the hoe had gone to work by itself and already dug up half the field for him. From that day on, Joseph Ciufolo was the happiest tiller alive: he would dig until he got tired, then take his flute out of his pocket, while the hoe went on digging by itself.

But Joseph Ciufolo worked for a stepfather who bore him no love and wished to turn him out of the house. In the beginning the man said Joseph was a good worker but lazy; next he said Joseph dug a whole lot but badly. Joseph Ciufolo therefore took his flute and left home.

He went around to all the landowners, but none of them would give him any work. Finally he met an old beggar, and asked him for work to keep body and soul together. 61

'Come along with me,' said the beggar, 'and we will share alms.'

So Joseph Ciufolo started going around with the beggar and singing:

> 'Succor us, please, please succor us,
> In the name of Jesus and all His Saints!'

Everybody gave alms to the old man, but to Joseph Ciufolo they all said, 'What's a young man like you doing out begging? Why don't you work for a living?'

'Nobody will hire me,' replied Joseph Ciufolo.

'That's what you say. There's the king with so many untilled fields that he's offering good wages to anyone willing to cultivate them.'

Joseph Ciufolo went to the king's fields and took the old man whose alms he had been sharing. The fields had never been worked by anyone. Joseph Ciufolo dug them up, sowed them, weeded them, then harvested the crops. Whenever he wearied of reaping he would play his flute; and once he was weary of playing, he would sing:

> 'Sickle so brisk, sickle so gay,
> Master's child with me, away!'

Hearing the singing, the princess looked out the window. She saw Joseph Ciufolo and fell in love with him. But she was a princess, and he a tiller; the king would never consent to their marriage. So they decided to run away together.

They fled at night in a boat. They were already on the high seas, when Joseph Ciufolo remembered the beggar. He said to his beloved, 'We must fetch the old man, since he shared his alms with me. I can't go off and leave him like that.' At that very moment they saw the old soul coming up behind the boat, walking on the water as if it had been dry land. Reaching the boat, he said, 'We agreed to divide everything we had, and I always shared with you everything I own. Now you have the king's daughter and must give half of her to me.' At that he handed Joseph Ciufolo a knife to cut his bride in half.

Joseph Ciufolo took the knife with a trembling hand. 'You are right,' he said, 'you are perfectly right.' He was on the point of cutting his bride in two, when the old man stopped him.

'Stop! I knew you were a just man. I am the dead man, mind you, whom you covered with green boughs. Go in peace, and may the two of you always be happy.'

The old man walked away on the waves. The boat came to an island rich in all good things, with a princely palace awaiting the newlyweds.

Misfortune

Once, so the story goes, there were seven children, all of them girls and daughters of a king and queen. War was declared on their father. He was captured and dethroned, while his wife and children were left to shift for themselves. To make ends meet, the queen gave up the palace, and they all squeezed into a hovel. Times were hard, and it was a miracle if they got anything to eat. One day a fruit vendor came by. The queen stopped him to buy a few figs. While she was making her purchase, an old woman passed, asking for alms. 'Goodness me!' said the queen. 'I wish I could help you, but I can't. I am poor too.'

'How do you happen to be poor?' asked the old woman.

'You don't know? I am the queen of Spain, humbled by the war waged against my husband.'

'You poor thing. But do you know why everything is going badly for you now? You have under your roof a daughter who is truly ill-starred. You'll never prosper again as long as she stays at home.'

'You don't mean I should send one of my daughters away?'

'Alas, my good lady, that's the only solution.'

'Who is this ill-starred daughter?'

'The one who sleeps with her hands crossed. Tonight while your daughters are sleeping, take a candle and go and look at them. The one you find with her hands crossed must be sent away. Only in that way will you recover your lost domains.'

At midnight the queen took the candle and filed past the beds of her seven daughters. They were all asleep, some with hands folded, others with their hands under their cheeks or pillows. She came to the last girl, who happened to be the youngest, and found her sleeping with her hands crossed. 'Oh, my poor daughter! I really am obliged to send you away.'

As she said that, the young lady awakened and saw her mother holding a candle and weeping. 'What's wrong, Mother?'

'Nothing, my daughter. An old beggar-woman happened by and explained that I'll prosper only after sending away that daughter of mine who sleeps with her hands crossed. The unfortunate girl turns out to be you!'

'That's all you're weeping over?' replied the daughter. 'I'll dress and leave at once.' She put her clothes on, tied her personal effects up in a bundle, and was off.

After going a great distance she came to a desolate
66 moor where only one house stood. She approached,

heard the sound of a loom, and saw some women weaving.

'Won't you come in?' said one of the weavers.

'Thank you.'

'What is your name?'

'Misfortune.'

'Would you like to work for us?'

'I certainly would.'

She set to work sweeping and doing the housework. In the evening, the women said to her, 'Listen, Misfortune, we are going out tonight. After we've locked the door on the outside, you are to lock it on the inside. When we return in the morning, we'll unlock it on the outside, and you'll unlock it on the inside. You must see that no one steals the silk, braiding, or cloth we have woven.' With that, they left.

When midnight struck, Misfortune heard a snipping of scissors. Candle in hand, she rushed to the loom and beheld a woman with a pair of scissors cutting all the gold cloth from the loom, and she realized her Evil Fate had followed her here. In the morning her mistresses returned; they unlocked the door from the outside, and she unlocked it from the inside. As soon as they came in, their eyes fell on the shreds littering the floor. 'You shameless wretch! Is this how you repay us for taking you in? Begone with you!' And they dismissed her with a kick.

Misfortune walked on through the countryside. Before entering a certain town, she stopped before a shop where they sold bread, vegetables, wine, and other things, and asked for alms. The shopkeeper's wife gave her a bit of bread and a glass of wine. When the shopkeeper returned, he took pity on her and told his wife to let her stay and sleep in the shop that night on the sacks. The shopkeeper and his wife slept upstairs, and in the middle of the night they heard a commotion below. Rushing downstairs to see what was going on, they found the casks uncorked and wine running all over the house. At that, the husband went looking for the girl and found her atop the sacks groaning as though caught in a nightmare. 'Shameless wretch! Only you could be responsible for all this mess!' He took a stick and beat her, then put her out of the shop.

Not knowing which way to turn, Misfortune ran off, weeping. At daybreak she met a woman doing her laundry.

'What are you looking at?'

'I'm lost.'

'Can you wash and iron?'

'Yes, indeed.'

'Well, stay and help me. I'll do the lathering and you'll do the rinsing.'

Misfortune began rinsing the clothes and hanging them

up to dry. As soon as they dried, she gathered them up to mend, starch, and press.

Now these clothes were the prince's. When he saw them, he was struck by how beautifully they had been done. 'Signora Francisca,' he said, 'you've never done such a good piece of work, I really must reward you for it.' And he gave her ten gold pieces.

Signora Francisca used the money to dress Misfortune up and buy a sack of flour to bake bread. Two of the loaves were ring-shaped and seasoned with anise and sesame seed. 'Take these two ring-shaped loaves to the seashore,' she told Misfortune, 'and call my Fate, like this – "Hallooooo! Fate of Signora Franciscaaaaa!" – three times. At the third call my Fate will appear, and you will give her a ring-shaped loaf and my regards. Then ask her where your own Fate is and do the same with her.'

Misfortune walked slowly to the seashore.

'Hallooooo! Fate of Signora Franciscaaaa! Hallooooo! Fate of Signora Franciscaaaaa! Hallooooo! Fate of Signora Franciscaaaaa!' Signora Francisca's Fate came out. Misfortune delivered the message, gave her the ring-shaped loaf, and then asked, 'Fate of Signora Francisca, would you be so gracious as to inform me of the whereabouts of my own Fate?'

'Hear me through: follow this mule trail a piece until you come to an oven. Beside the pit of oven-sweepings sits an old witch. Approach her gently and give her the ring-shaped loaf, for she is your Fate. She will refuse it and insult you. But leave the bread for her and come away.'

At the oven Misfortune found the old woman, who was so foul, bleary-eyed, and smelly that the girl was almost nauseated. 'Dear Fate of mine, will you do me the honor of accepting –' she began, offering her the bread.

'Away with you! Be gone! Who asked you for bread?' And she turned her back on the girl. Misfortune put the loaf down and returned to Signora Francisca's.

The next day was Monday, washday. Signora Francisca put the clothes in to soak, then lathered them. Misfortune scrubbed and rinsed them; when they were dry, she mended and ironed them. When the ironing was finished, Signora Francisca put everything in a basket and carried it to the palace. Seeing the clothes, the king said, 'Signora Francisca, you won't pretend you've ever washed and ironed that nicely before!' For her pains, he gave her ten more gold pieces.

Signora Francisca bought more flour, made two ring-shaped loaves again, and sent Misfortune off with them to their Fates.

The next time she did his wash, the prince, who was getting married and anxious to have his clothes perfectly 70 laundered for the event, rewarded Signora Francisca with twenty gold pieces. This time Signora Francisca bought not only flour for two loaves; for Misfortune's Fate she purchased an elegant dress with a hoop skirt, a petticoat, dainty handkerchiefs, and a comb and pomade for her hair, not to mention other odds and ends.

Misfortune walked to the oven. 'Dear Fate of mine, here is your ring-shaped loaf.'

The Fate, who was growing tamer, came forward grumbling to take the bread. Then Misfortune reached out and grabbed her and proceeded to wash her with soap and water. Next she did her hair and dressed her up from head to foot in her new finery. The Fate at first writhed like a snake, but seeing herself all spick-and-span she became a different person entirely. 'Listen to me, Misfortune,' she said. 'For all your kindness to me, I'm making you a present of this little box,' and she handed her a box as tiny as those which contain wax matches.

Misfortune went flying home to Signora Francisca and opened the little box. In it lay a piece of braid. They were both somewhat disappointed. 'What a piece of nothing!' they said, and stuffed the braid away in the bottom of a drawer.

The following week when Signora Francisca took the clean wash back to the palace, she found the prince quite depressed. Being on familiar terms with him, the washerwoman asked, 'What's the matter, my prince?'

'What's the matter? Here I am all ready to get married, and now we find out that my betrothed's bridal gown lacks a piece of braid which cannot be matched anywhere in the kingdom.'

'Wait a minute, Majesty,' said Signora Francisca, and ran home, rummaged through the drawer, and came back to the prince with that special piece of braid. They compared it with what was on the bridal dress: it was identical.

The prince said, 'You have saved the day for me, and I intend to pay you the weight of this piece of braid in gold.'

He took a pair of scales, placing the braid in one plate and gold in the other. But no amount of gold made the scales balance. He then tried measuring the braid's weight with a steel yard, but this too was unsuccessful.

'Signora Francisca,' he said, 'be honest. How can a little piece of braid possibly weigh so much? Where did you get it?'

Signora Francisca had no alternative but to tell the whole story, and the prince then wanted to see Misfortune. The washerwoman dressed her up (they had gradually accumulated a little finery) and took her to the palace. Misfortune entered the throne room and gave a royal curtsy; she was a monarch's daughter and by no means ignorant of courtly decorum. The prince welcomed her, offered her a seat, then asked, 'But who are you?'

'I am the youngest daughter of the king of Spain, who was dethroned and imprisoned. My bad luck forced me out into the world where I have endured insults, contempt, and many beatings' – and she told him all.

The first thing the prince did was send for the weavers whose silk and braid the Evil Fate had cut up. 'How much did this damage cost you?'

'Two hundred gold crowns.'

'Here are your two hundred gold crowns. Let me tell you that this poor maiden you cast out is the daughter of a king and queen. That is all, be gone!'

Next he summoned the owners of the shop where the Evil Fate had tapped the casks. 'And how much damage did you suffer?'

'Three hundred crowns' worth.'

'Here are your three hundred crowns. But think twice next time before thrashing a poor king's daughter. Now out of my sight!'

He dismissed his original betrothed and married Misfortune. For matron of honor he gave her Signora Francisca.

Let us leave the happy couple and turn our attention to Misfortune's mother. After her daughter's departure, fortune's wheel began to turn in her favor: one day her brother and nephews arrived at the head of a mighty army and reconquered the kingdom. The queen and her children moved back into their old palace and all the comforts and luxuries they had formerly enjoyed. But in the back of their minds they thought of the youngest daughter, of whom they had heard absolutely nothing in all the time she had been gone. Meanwhile the prince, upon learning that Misfortune's mother had regained her kingdom, sent messengers to inform her of his marriage to her daughter. Ever so pleased, the mother set out for her daughter's with knights and ladies-in-waiting. Likewise with knights and ladies-in-waiting, the daughter rode to meet her mother. They met at the border, embraced over and over, with the seven sisters standing around, every bit as moved as their mother, while there was great rejoicing in one kingdom and the other.

Jump into My Sack

Many, many years ago, in the barren mountains of Niolo, lived a father with twelve sons. A famine was raging, and the father said, 'My sons, I have no more bread to give you. Go out into the world, where you will certainly fare better than here at home.'

The eleven older boys were getting ready to leave, when the twelfth and youngest, who was lame, started weeping. 'And what will a cripple like me do to earn his bread?'

'My child,' said his father, 'don't cry. Go with your brothers, and what they earn will be yours as well.'

So the twelve promised to stay together always and departed. They walked a whole day, then a second, and the little lame boy fell constantly behind. On the third day, the oldest brother said, 'Our little brother Francis, who's always lagging, is nothing but a nuisance! Let's walk off and leave him on the road. That will be best for him too, for some kind-hearted soul will come along and take pity on him.'

So they stopped no more to wait for him to catch up, but walked on, asking alms of everyone they met, all the way to Bonifacio.

In Bonifacio they saw a boat moored at the dock. 'What if we climbed in and sailed to Sardinia?' said the oldest boy. 'Maybe there's less hunger there than in our land.'

The brothers got into the boat and set sail. When they were halfway across the straits, a fierce storm arose and the boat was dashed to pieces on the reefs, and all eleven brothers drowned.

Meanwhile the little cripple Francis, exhausted and frantic when he missed his brothers, screamed and cried and then fell asleep by the roadside. The fairy guardian of that particular spot had seen and heard everything from a treetop. As soon as Francis was asleep, she came down the tree, picked certain special herbs, and prepared a plaster, which she smoothed on the lame leg; immediately the leg became sound. Then she disguised herself as a poor little old woman and sat down on a bundle of firewood to wait for Francis to wake up.

Francis awakened, got up, prepared to limp off, and then realized he was no longer lame but could walk like everyone else. He saw the little old woman sitting there, and asked, 'Madam, have you by chance seen a doctor around here?'

'A doctor? What do you want with a doctor?'

'I want to thank him. A great doctor must certainly have come by while I was sleeping and cured my lame leg.'

'I am the one who cured your lame leg,' replied the little old woman, 'since I know all about herbs, including the one that heals lame legs.'

As pleased as Punch, Francis threw his arms around the little old woman and kissed her on both cheeks. 'How can I thank you, ma'am? Here, let me carry your bundle of wood for you.'

He bent over to pick up the bundle, but when he stood up, he faced not the old woman, but the most beautiful maiden imaginable, all radiant with diamonds and blond hair down to her waist; she wore a deep blue dress embroidered with gold, and two stars of precious stones sparkled on her ankle-boots. Dumbfounded, Francis fell at the fairy's feet.

'Get up,' she said. 'I am well aware that you are grateful, and I shall help you. Make two wishes, and I will grant them at once. I am the queen of the fairies of Lake Creno, mind you.'

The boy thought a bit, then replied, 'I desire a sack that will suck in whatever I name.'

'And just such a sack shall you have. Now make one more wish.'

'I desire a stick that will do whatever I command.'

'And just such a stick shall you have,' replied the fairy, and vanished. At Francis's feet lay a sack and a stick.

Overjoyed, the boy decided to try them out. Being

hungry, he cried, 'A roasted partridge into my sack!' Zoom! A partridge fully roasted flew into the sack. 'Along with bread!' Zoom! A loaf of bread came sailing into the sack. 'Also a bottle of wine!' Zoom! There was the bottle of wine. Francis ate a first-rate meal.

Then he set out again, limping no longer, and the next day he found himself in Mariana, where the most famous gamblers of Corsica and the Continent were meeting. Francis didn't have a cent to his name, so he ordered, 'One hundred thousand crowns into my sack!' and the sack filled with crowns. The news spread like wildfire through Mariana that the fabulously wealthy prince of Santo Francesco had arrived.

At that particular time, mind you, the Devil was especially partial to the city of Mariana. Disguised as a handsome young man, he beat everybody at cards, and when the players ran out of money, he would purchase their souls. Hearing of this rich foreigner who went by the name of prince of Santo Francesco, the Devil in disguise approached him without delay. 'Noble prince, pardon my boldness in coming to you, but your fame as a gambler is so great that I couldn't resist calling on you.'

'You put me to shame,' replied Francis. 'To tell the truth, I don't know how to play any game at all, nor have I ever had a deck of cards in my hand. However, I would be happy to play a hand with you, just for the sake of learning the game, and I'm sure that with you as a teacher I'll be an expert in no time.'

The Devil was so gratified by the visit that, upon taking leave and bowing goodbye, he negligently stretched out a leg and showed his cloven hoof. 'Oh, me!' said Francis to himself. 'So this is old Satan himself who has honored me with a visit. Very well, he will meet his match.' Once more alone, he commanded of the sack a fine dinner.

The next day Francis went to the casino. There was a great turmoil, with all the people crowded around one particular spot. Francis pushed through and saw, on the ground, the body of a young man with a blood-stained chest. 'He was a gambler,' someone explained, 'who lost his entire fortune and thrust a dagger into his heart, not a minute ago.'

All the gamblers were sad-faced. But one, noted Francis, stood in their midst laughing up his sleeve; it was the Devil who had paid Francis a visit.

'Quick!' said the Devil, 'let's take this unfortunate man out, and get on with the game!' And they all picked up their cards once more.

Francis, who didn't even know how to hold the cards in his hand, lost everything he had with him that day. By the second day he knew a little bit about the game, but lost still more than the day before. By the third day he was an 79 expert, and lost so much that everyone was sure he was ruined. But the loss did not trouble him in the least, since there was his sack he could command and then find inside all the money he needed.

He lost so much that the Devil thought to himself, He might have been the richest man in existence to start with, but he's surely about to end up now with nothing to his name. 'Noble prince,' he said, taking him aside, 'I can't tell you how sorry I am over the misfortune that has befallen you. But I have good news for you: heed my words and you will recover half of what you lost!'

'How?'

The Devil looked around, then whispered, 'Sell me your soul!'

'Ah!' cried Francis. 'So that's your advice to me, Satan? Go on, jump into my sack!'

The Devil smirked and aimed to flee, but there was no escape: he flew head-first into the yawning sack, which Francis closed, then addressed the stick, 'Now pound him for all you're worth!'

Blows rained fast and furious. Inside, the Devil writhed, cried, cursed. 'Let me out! Let me out! Stop, or you'll kill me!'

'Really? You'll give up the ghost? Would that be a loss, do you think?' And the stick went right on beating him.

After three hours of that shower, Francis spoke. 'That will do, at least for today.'

'What will you take in return for setting me free?' asked the Devil in a weak voice.

'Listen carefully: if you want your freedom back, you must bring back to life at once every one of those poor souls who killed themselves in the casino because of you!'

'It's a bargain!' replied the Devil.

'Come on out, then. But remember, I can catch you again any time I feel like it.'

The Devil dared not go back on his word. He disappeared underground and, in almost no time, up came a throng of young men pale of face and with feverish eyes. 'My friends,' said Francis, 'you ruined yourselves gambling, and the only way out was to kill yourselves. I was able to have you brought back this time, but I might not be able to do so another time. Will you promise me to gamble no more?'

'Yes, yes, we promise!'

'Fine! Here are a thousand crowns for each of you. Go in peace, and earn your bread honestly.'

Overjoyed, the revived youths departed, some returning to families in mourning, others striking out on their own, their past misdeeds having been the death of their parents.

Francis, too, thought of his old father. He set out for 81

his village but, along the way, met a boy wringing his hands in despair.

'How now, young man? Do you make wry faces for sale?' asked Francis, in high spirits. 'How much are they by the dozen?'

'I don't feel like laughing, sir,' replied the boy.

'What's the matter?'

'My father's a woodcutter and the sole support of our family. This morning he fell out of a chestnut tree and broke his arm. I ran into town for the doctor, but he knows we are poor and refused to come.'

'Is that all that's worrying you? Set your mind at rest. I'll take care of things.'

'You're a doctor?'

'No, but I'll make that one come. What is his name?'

'Doctor Pancrazio.'

'Fine! Dr Pancrazio, jump into my sack!'

Into the sack, head-first, went a doctor with all his instruments.

'Stick, pound him for all you're worth!' And the stick began its dance. 'Help! Mercy!'

'Do you promise to cure the woodcutter free of charge?'

'I promise whatever you ask.'

'Get out of the sack, then.' And the doctor ran to the

woodcutter's bedside.

Francis continued on his way and, in a few days, came to his village, where even greater hunger now raged than before. By constantly repeating, 'Into my sack a roasted chicken, a bottle of wine,' Francis managed to provision an inn where all could go and eat their fill without paying a penny.

He did this for as long as the famine lasted. But he stopped, once times of plenty returned, so as not to encourage laziness.

Do you think he was happy, though? Of course not! He was sad without any news of his eleven brothers. He had long since forgiven them for running off and leaving him, a helpless cripple. He tried saying, 'Brother John, jump into my sack!'

Something stirred inside the sack. Francis opened it and found a heap of bones.

'Brother Paul, jump into my sack!'

Another heap of bones.

'Brother Peter, jump into my sack!' Calling them all, up to the eleventh, he found each time, alas, only a little pile of bones half gnawed in two. There was no doubt about it: his brothers had all died together.

Francis was sad. His father also died, leaving him all alone. Then it was his turn to grow old.

His last remaining desire before dying was to see again the fairy of Lake Creno who had made him so prosperous.

He therefore set out and reached the place where he had first met her. He waited and waited, but the fairy did not come. 'Where are you, good queen? Please appear one more time! I can't die until I've seen you again!'

Night had fallen and there was still no sign of the fairy. Instead, here came Death down the road. In one hand she held a black banner and, in the other, her scythe. She approached Francis, saying, 'Well, old man, are you not yet weary of life? Haven't you been over enough hills and dales? Isn't it time you did as everyone else and came along with me?'

'O, Death,' replied old Francis. 'Bless you! Yes, I have seen enough of the world and everything in it; I have had my fill of everything. But before coming with you, I must first bid someone farewell. Allow me one more day.'

'Say your prayers, if you don't want to die like a heathen, and hurry after me.'

'Please, wait until the cock crows in the morning.'

'No.'

'Just one hour more, then?'

'Not even one minute more.'

'Since you are so cruel, then, jump into my sack!'

Death shuddered, all her bones rattled, but she had no choice but jump into the sack. In the same instant appeared the queen of the fairies, as radiant and youthful as

the first time. 'Fairy,' said Francis, 'I thank you!' Then he addressed Death: 'Jump out of the sack and attend to me.'

'You have never abused the power I gave you, Francis,' said the fairy. 'Your sack and your stick have always been put to good use. I shall reward you, if you tell me what you would like.'

'I have no more desires.'

'Would you like to be a chieftain?'

'No.'

'Would you like to be king?'

'I wish nothing more.'

'Now that you're an old man, would you like health and youth again?'

'I have seen you, and I'm content to die.'

'Farewell, Francis. But first burn the sack and the stick.' And the fairy vanished.

The good Francis built a big fire, warmed his frozen limbs briefly, then threw the sack and the stick into the flames, so that no one could put them to evil use.

Death was hiding behind a bush. 'Cockadoodledo! Cockadoodledo!' crowed the first cock.

Francis did not hear. Age had made him deaf.

'There's the cock crowing!' announced Death, and struck the old man with her scythe. Then she vanished, bearing his mortal remains.

MARTIN AMIS · *God's Dice*
HANS CHRISTIAN ANDERSEN · *The Emperor's New Clothes*
MARCUS AURELIUS · *Meditations*
JAMES BALDWIN · *Sonny's Blues*
AMBROSE BIERCE · *An Occurrence at Owl Creek Bridge*
DIRK BOGARDE · *From Le Pigeonnier*
WILLIAM BOYD · *Killing Lizards*
POPPY Z. BRITE · *His Mouth will Taste of Wormwood*
ITALO CALVINO · *Ten Italian Folktales*
ALBERT CAMUS · *Summer*
TRUMAN CAPOTE · *First and Last*
RAYMOND CHANDLER · *Goldfish*
ANTON CHEKHOV · *The Black Monk*
ROALD DAHL · *Lamb to the Slaughter*
ELIZABETH DAVID · *I'll be with You in the Squeezing of a Lemon*
N. J. DAWOOD (TRANS.) · *The Seven Voyages of Sindbad the Sailor*
ISAK DINESEN · *The Dreaming Child*
SIR ARTHUR CONAN DOYLE · *The Man with the Twisted Lip*
DICK FRANCIS · *Racing Classics*
SIGMUND FREUD · *Five Lectures on Psycho-Analysis*
KAHLIL GIBRAN · *Prophet, Madman, Wanderer*
STEPHEN JAY GOULD · *Adam's Navel*
ALASDAIR GRAY · *Five Letters from an Eastern Empire*
GRAHAM GREENE · *Under the Garden*
JAMES HERRIOT · *Seven Yorkshire Tales*
PATRICIA HIGHSMITH · *Little Tales of Misogyny*
M. R. JAMES AND R. L. STEVENSON · *The Haunted Dolls' House*
RUDYARD KIPLING · *Baa Baa, Black Sheep*
PENELOPE LIVELY · *A Long Night at Abu Simbel*
KATHERINE MANSFIELD · *The Escape*

PENGUIN 60s